# HOUGHTON MIFFLIN
# Reading

# Spring Is Here

## HOUGHTON MIFFLIN

BOSTON

Printed in the U.S.A.

ISBN: 0-618-16195-3

6789-BS-06 05 04 03

Design, Art Management, and Page Production: Studio Goodwin Sturges

# Contents

# Get Set! Play!

by Ann Spivey
illustrated by Darcia Labrosse

 can get wet.
"Not I," said

2

Pig can get wet.
"Not I," said Pig.

Fox can get wet.
"Not I," said Fox.

 got a  .

Pig got  .

Fox got 3 .
Get set! Play!

# Ben

by Ann Spivey
illustrated by Susan Calitri

"My pet!" said Ben.
"I can not get it."

"Get a net," said the vet.
Ben can not get it yet.

"Get a box," said Fox.
Ben can not get it yet.

"Get ten men," said Hen.

Ben got ten men.

Ten men got it.
Ben can play.

# Pig Can Get Wet

by Ann Spivey

illustrated by Vincent Andriani

"My big wig can not get wet,"
said Pig.  Pig sat.

"My big wig can not get wet."
Cat sat.

Cat can sit. Pig can sit.
A big  can not sit.

Cat got wet.
Pig got wet.

"A pig **can** get wet," she said.
"A pig can play."

# Word List

---

### *Get Set! Play!*

**DECODABLE WORDS**

## Target Skills
Consonant *w:*
wet

**Short *e:***
get, set, wet

**Words Using Previously Taught Skills**
can, Fox, get, got, not, Pig, set, wet

**HIGH-FREQUENCY WORDS**

**New**
play

**Previously Taught**
a, I, said

---

### *Ben*

**DECODABLE WORDS**

## Target Skill
Consonant *y:*
yet

**Words Using Previously Taught Skills**
Ben, box, can, Fox, get, got, Hen, it, men, net, not, pet, ten, vet, yet

**HIGH-FREQUENCY WORDS**

**New**
she

**Previously Taught**
a, I, my, play, said, the

# Pig Can Get Wet

## DECODABLE WORDS

### Words Using Previously Taught Skills
big, can, Cat, get, got, not, Pig, sat, sit, wet, wig

## HIGH-FREQUENCY WORDS

### Previously Taught
a, my, play, said, she

## HIGH-FREQUENCY WORDS TAUGHT TO DATE

| a | have | like | see |
|-----|------|------|-----|
| and | here | my | she |
| for | I | play | the |
| go | is | said | to |

*Decoding Skills Taught to Date* Consonant *b*, consonant *c*, consonant *d*, consonant *f*, consonant *g*, consonant *h*, consonant *k*, consonant *l*, consonant *m*, consonant *n*, consonant *q*, consonant *r*, consonant *s*, consonant *t*, consonant *v*, consonant *w*, consonant *x*, consonant *y*, consonant *z*, short *a*, short *e*, short *i*, short *o*